# The Trouble with Tippers

This edition published in 2002
by Armadillo Books
an imprint of
Bookmart Limited
Registered Number 2372865
Trading as Bookmart Limited
Desford Road
Enderby
Leicester
LE9 5AD

ISBN 1-84322-093-8

Printed in China

# Starting to read – no trouble!

The troublesome tipper in this story helps to make
sharing books at home successful and enjoyable.
The book can be used in several ways to help
beginning readers gain confidence.

You could start by reading the illustrated words
at the edge of each lefthand page with your
child. Have fun trying to spot the same words in
the story itself.

All the words on the righthand pages have already
been met on the facing page. Help your child to
read these by pointing out words and groups of
words already met.

Finally, all the illustrated words can be found
at the end of the book. Enjoy checking all the
words you can both read!

# The
# Trouble
# with
# Tippers

Written by Nicola Baxter · Illustrated by Geoff Ball

ARMADILLO

**tipper**

On the building site, everything is very quiet.

**digger**

**cement mixer**

The tipper is not tipping.

The digger is not digging.

The cement mixer is not mixing.

**builders**

The builders are not building.

They are having a break.

# The Trouble with

# Tippers

Written by Nicola Baxter · Illustrated by Geoff Ball

ARMADILLO

On the building site, everything is very quiet.

**tipper**

**digger**

**cement mixer**

**builders**

The tipper is not tipping.

The digger is not digging.

The cement mixer is not mixing.

The builders are not building.

They are having a break.

The builders are very quiet!

**van**

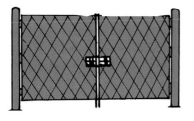

**gate**

**foreman**

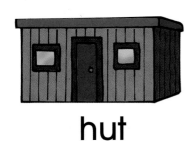

**hut**

Brrrm! Brrrrm! Who is this?

A red van comes through the gate.

The foreman is back!

He gets out of the car and strides over to the builders' hut. He does **not** look happy.

"Get to work!" he yells.
"And hurry!"

The builders hurry back to work!

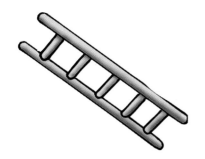

**ladder**

Now the builders are building in a hurry.

The cement mixer is mixing in a hurry.

The digger is digging in a hurry.

**bucket**

The tipper is tipping in a hurry – too much of a hurry!

Oh no! The tipper hits a ladder! It hits a bucket! It hits a **car**!

**car**

**architect**

Who is this? It is the architect.

The architect is **not** happy.

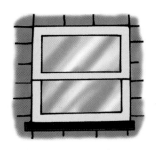

**window**

**door**

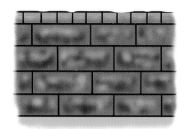

**wall**

**plan**

The architect strides around the building site. Everything seems to be wrong.

"This window is too big!" she says.

She says the door is too small.
The wall is too high.
The roof is too low.

She looks at her plan.
She doesn't look where she is going!

"And this is wrong, too!" she says.

**hole**

**sand**

**hard hat**

**spade**

"Fill in this hole **now**!" shouts the architect.

The tipper hurries forward. It tips a load of sand. Oh no!

"Help!" shouts a builder, holding on to his hard hat.

"Help!" shouts another builder, holding on to his spade.

"Help!' shouts the architect, holding on to her plan.

Now the tipper is in the hole!

**rope**

The builders try to pull the tipper out with a rope.

**chain**

**phone**

The digger tries to pull the tipper out with a chain.

"It's no good," says the foreman. "Where is my phone? We need a crane to lift it out."

**crane**

The crane lifts the tipper out.

**mugs**

**newspapers**

**sandwiches**

**watch**

"Now we can get to work at last!" says the architect, looking at her watch.

But everything is very quiet on the building site.

The builders are not building. They are drinking mugs of tea, reading newspapers and eating sandwiches.

After all that trouble, it's time for a break!

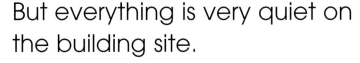

And the tipper is having a break too!

# Picture dictionary

Now you can read these words!

architect

bucket

builders

car

cement mixer

chain

crane

digger

door

foreman

gate

hard hat

hole

hut

ladder

mugs

newspapers

phone

plan

rope

sand

sandwiches

spade

van

wall

watch

window